KU-428-768

Schools Library and Information Service

S00000630903

The Houseminders

Written by
Ian Whybrow

Illustrated by
Julie Monks

Hodder
Children's
Books

A division of Hodder Headline Limited

DUDLEY PUBLIC LIBRARIES

L   4574 6

630903   SCH

JY WHY

Leaves were **falling** for Paul and Didi's first time at **the** new house.

Dad let Paul turn the
big old key.
So he was first in
through the
back door.

Paul said it was a dark
place with a sad smell.
And could they go home now?

Mum said not to mind
the sad smell.
That was only because
the house was empty.

It would take a bit
of time, but they would
fix it up and
make it special.

Paul didn't like the bare
walls and floors.
But Didi said to look
out of the window.
There were fields and hills
and hills and fields.

And were those cows?
And sheep, look!
What about that one
standing on its back legs
eating the hedge!
Paul liked the funny sheep.

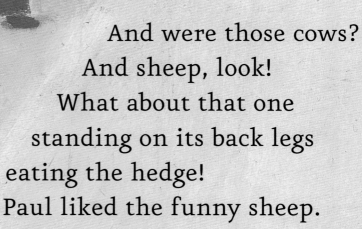

But he said to
Didi in a whisper,
'I hate empty houses.'
Didi whispered back,
'Do you want to know a secret?
Come on, I'll show you'

'The secret is, this house is never really empty,' Didi said, 'because there are minders to mind it while we're not here.'

Didi turned the
cushion on the old
chair over and showed
Paul two field mice,
very quiet,
very still.
Watching.

So that was how Paul
met the **autumn minders**
of the house . . .

The next time at
the house there was
snOW
all
over . . .

When Paul saw the chair
thrown out in the yard for
rubbish he began to cry.

Didi said not to worry, the mice
would be safe somewhere.
And she was sure there
were winter minders
in the house now,
so they'd better start looking . . .

They looked and looked.
Nothing.
Then Dad called from the loft,
'Who's going to help me stop these
water pipes from freezing?'

Paul and Didi climbed
the ladder.

Paul had
the torch to shine.
Now Dad could see
to wrap up the pipes
to keep them warm.

Up on the pipes, two
little bats were
clinging together.

'They can be the winter
minders,' whispered Didi.
That was another nice
secret to have . . .

Next time at
the house there were
honeysuckle
and
builders . . .

There were geese and goslings next door.
And lambs with the sheep on the hill.
And calves with the cows in the field.

Then the **martins**
came diving by
trying to find some mud.
But the mud was too dry
for nest building.

Good thing Didi and Paul
had their boots on.
They **pulled** out the hose
and made
a little mudpool under
the apple trees.

Later the martins **came** SWOOPing for beakfuls of nest-mud.

And Paul and Didi
and Mum and Dad
sat on the brick pile
watching them build
their mud nests.
Paul knew
just what the birds were.
'That's our

spring minders!'

he whispered in Didi's ear.

Next time
at the **house**
they came with
the **moving van** ...

Paul's job was with Didi,
minding the cats and
the guinea pigs.
And showing the
moving-men their special
new home.

So that day the dark places became bright places.
And the sad smell became a happy smell. The house had new
paint and wallpaper, and carpets and cupboards and everything.
And it had plenty of minders
to keep it company.

So which were
the best minders,
do you think?

Was it the **field mice**
safe and tight in
the hole in the farmyard wall?

Was it **the bats**
that chased the **bugs**
round and round
the house in the
summer moonlight?

Was it the **busy martins** snug in their mud nest under the eaves?

Or was it this tired **little boy and his sister** who fell asleep on the sofa minding the cats?

For Joan and Dennis,
the minders of Ladylift
I.W.

To Kieran
J.M.

THE HOUSEMINDERS
by Ian Whybrow and Julie Monks
British Library Cataloguing in Publication Data
A catalogue record of this book is available from the British Library.

ISBN 0 340 764708 (HB)
ISBN 0 340 76471 6 (PB)

Text copyright © Ian Whybrow 2000
Illustrations copyright © Julie Monks 2000

The right of Ian Whybrow to be identified as the author of this Work
and of Julie Monks to be identified as the illustrator of this Work
has been asserted by them in accordance with
the Copyright, Designs and Patents Act 1988.

First edition published 2001
10 9 8 7 6 5 4 3 2 1

Published by Hodder Children's Books,
a division of Hodder Headline Limited,
338 Euston Road, London NW1 3BH

Printed in Hong Kong

All rights reserved